# NIGHT of the CRASH-TEST DUMMIES

**Other Books in The Far Side series**
The Far Side
Beyond The Far Side
In Search of The Far Side
Bride of The Far Side
Valley of The Far Side
It Came from The Far Side
Hound of The Far Side
The Far Side Observer
Wildlife Preserves
Wiener Dog Art
Unnatural Selections
Cows of Our Planet
The Chickens Are Restless
The Curse of Madame "C"


**Anthologies**

The Far Side Gallery
The Far Side Gallery 2
The Far Side Gallery 3
The Far Side Gallery 4
The PreHistory of The Far Side:
A 10th Anniversary Exhibit

# NIGHT of the CRASH-TEST DUMMIES

## A Far Side Collection
## by Gary Larson

WARNER BOOKS

A *Warner* Book

First published in Great Britain in 1989 by Futura Books
Reprinted 1989, 1990 (twice), 1991
This edition published by Warner Books in 1993
Reprinted 1993, 1994

Copyright © 1988 by Universal Press Syndicate

The moral right of the author has been asserted

A CIP catalogue record of this book is available from the British Library

ISBN 0 7515 0689 3

Printed and bound in Great Britain by
BPC Hazell Books Ltd
A member of
The British Printing Company Ltd

Warner Books
A Division of
Little, Brown and Company (UK)
Brettenham House
Lancaster Place
London WC2E 7EN

# NIGHT of the CRASH-TEST DUMMIES

Animal Camouflage

The rural professional and his cowphone

"Oh, wonderful! Look at this, Etta —
another mouth to feed."

"For crying out loud, I was *hibernating*! ...
Don't you guys ever take a pulse?"

"He told you *that?* Well, he's pulling your flagellum, Nancy."

"Hey, bucko ... I'm *through* begging."

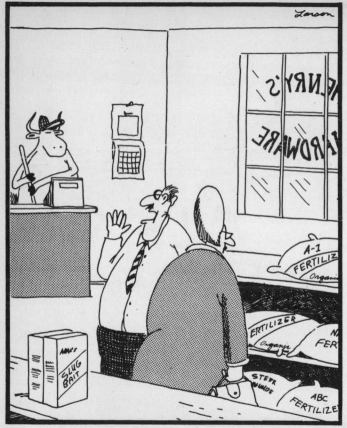

"Hey, Johnny! This lady wants to know the difference in all these fertilizers!"

Through some unfortunate celestial error, Ernie is sent to Hog Heaven.

The Bluebird of Happiness long absent from his life, Ned is visited by the Chicken of Depression.

"Oh my God! It's from Connie! She's written me a 'John deer' letter!"

11

"So! Planning on roaming the neighborhood
with some of your buddies today?"

"And *you*, Johnson! You stick with your man
and keep that hand in his *face*!"

Single-cell bars

Where beef jerky comes from

"Now go to sleep, Kevin — or once again I'll have to knock three times and summon the Floating Head of Death."

14

"Ah, yes, Mr. Frischberg, I thought you'd come ... but which of us is the *real* duck, Mr. Frischberg, and not just an illusion?"

15

That evening, with her blinds pulled, Mary had three helpings of corn, two baked potatoes, extra bread, and a little lamb.

"No, wait! *That's* not Uncle Floyd! Who is that? ... Criminy, I think it's just an air bubble!"

Bird cellars

"Hold it right there, Henry! ... You ain't plannin' on takin' that wrinkled horse into town, are you?"

"Frankly, you've got a lot of anger toward the world to work out, Mr. Pembrose."

Suddenly, throwing the festivities into utter confusion, Ujang begins to play "Stardust."

School for the Mechanically Declined

The Lone Ranger, long since retired, makes an unpleasant discovery.

At the Vincent van Gogh School of Art

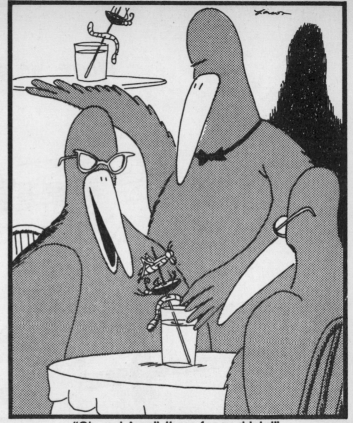

"Oh, my! Aren't *these* fancy drinks!"

"Say, Will — why don't you pull that thing out and play us a tune?"

...but the Secretary of State declined to comment on the latest round of talks... ...And today the A-1 Life Raft Co. issued a statement recalling 50,000 of its small rubber boats due to defective glue used in their manufacture, causing the boats to lose air and gradually sink over a matter of a few days... And now let's go to Lou Jackson for what's happening in sports...

The famous "Mr. Ed. vs. Francis the Talking Mule" debates

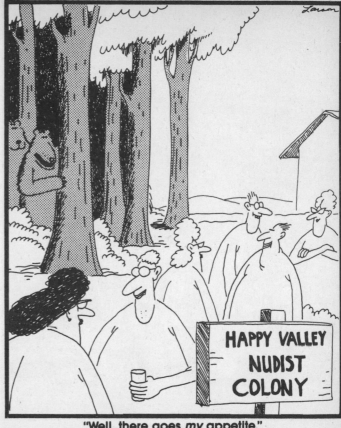

"Well, there goes *my* appetite."

"So then, when Old MacDonald turned his back,
I took that ax, and with a whack whack here
and a whack whack there, I finished him off."

"Ernie! Look what you're doing
— take those shoes off!"

Secret tools of the common crow

The townsfolk all stopped and stared; they didn't know the tall stranger who rode calmly through their midst, but they did know the reign of terror had ended.

"Bob and Ruth! Come on in. ... Have you met Russell and Bill, our 1.5 children?"

28

The Potatoheads in Paris

"Johnson, back off! It's an *Armandia lidderdalii*, all right — but it's rabid!"

"Well, let's see. . . . So far I've got rhythm and I've got music . . . actually, who could ask for anything more?"

"Beats me how they did it ... I got the whole thing at a garage sale for five bucks — and that included the stand."

**Embarrassing moments at gene parties**

**Fruitcases**

*In the Fly House of Horrors*

When ornithologists are mutually attracted

"That's a lie, Morty! ... Mom says you might have got the brains in the family, but *I* got the looks!"

**Night of the Potato Bugs**

**How fishermen blow their own minds**

Although troubled as a child, Zorro, as is well known, ultimately found his niche in history.

And then, just as he predicted, Thag became the channeler for a two million-year-old gibbon named Gus.

_Sled chickens of the North_

Jazz at the Wool Club

What really happened to Elvis

"Anytime, Slim."

Rocking the anthropological world, a second "Lucy" is discovered in southern Uganda.

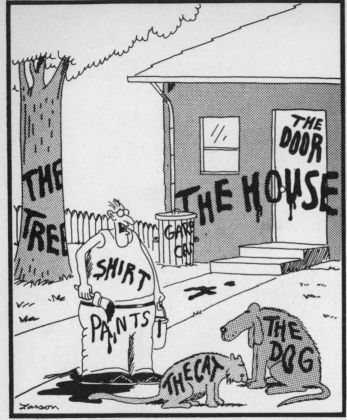

"Now! ... *That* should clear up
a few things around here!"

Cartoon readings

The committee to decide whether
spawning should be taught in school

"Green blood? I *hate* green blood."

Baryshnikov's ultimate nightmare

All day long, a tough gang of astrophysicists would monopolize the telescope and intimidate the other researchers.

At the popular dog film, *Man Throwing Sticks*

"Mind? Hey, buddy, these flat feet kept me out of the Army!"

Metamorphosis Nightclubs

The squid family on vacation

"Clean it up? Clean it up? Criminy, it's *supposed* to be a rathole!"

At the Old Spiders' Home

Rusty makes his move.

47

"Hey, I'm not *crazy* ... sure, I let him drive once in a while, but he's never, *never* off this leash for even a second."

"Mom! The kids at school say we're a family of Nerdenthals! ... Is that true?"

When chickens dream

"OK. I'll go back and tell my people that you're staying in the boat, but I warn you they're *not* going to like it."

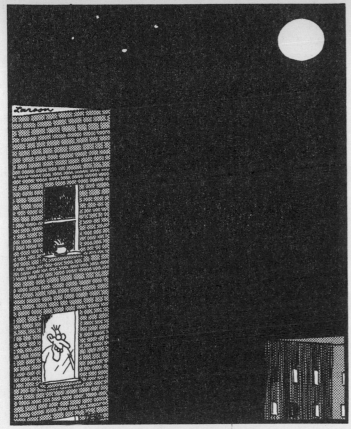

Full moon and empty head

Just as Dale entered the clearing and discovered, standing together, the Loch Ness monster, Bigfoot, and Jackie Onassis, his camera jammed.

**Hell's library**

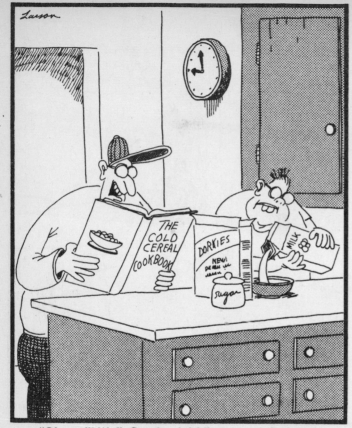

"Oh, wait! Wait, Cory! ... Add the cereal *first* and
*then* the milk!"

Early microbiologists

54

With their parents away, the young dragons
would stay up late lighting their sneezes.

"Well, down I go."

Piglet practical jokes

"Hey, you wanna see a *real* scar?
Check *this* baby out!"

56

"Well, the defendant and I had made this
deal in which we both prospered. ...
One of those 'you-scratch-me-behind-my-ears-
I'll-scratch-you-behind-yours' arrangements."

"Oh, don't be silly! No thanks needed.
Just take the brain — but tell that doctor
you work for not to be such a stranger."

**Parakeet furniture**

**How bears relax**

Canine comedians

"It's a letter from Julio in America. ...
His banana bunch arrived safely and he's
living in the back room of some grocery store."

Nerds in hell

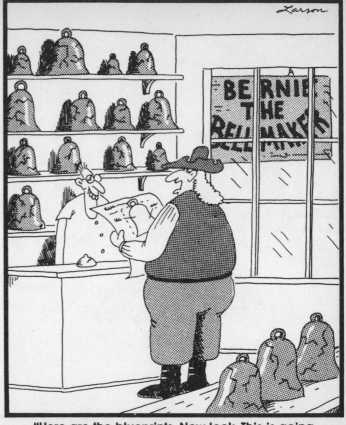

"Here are the blueprints. Now look: This is going to be the *Liberty* Bell, so we obviously expect that it be forged with great diligence and skill."

"When I got home, Harold's coat and hat were gone, his worries were on the doorstep, and Gladys Mitchell, my neighbor, says she saw him heading west on the sunny side of the street."

63

Songwriters of the Old West

"Listen. I've *tried* to communicate with him, but he's like a broken record: 'None of your bee's wax, none of your bee's wax.'"

*Punk flamingoes*

"Drive, George, drive! This
one's got a coat hanger!"

"What the hey? ... Someone's
shortsheeted my bed again!"

"Tough break, Rusty. ... Seven years bad luck — of course, in your case, that works out to 49 years."

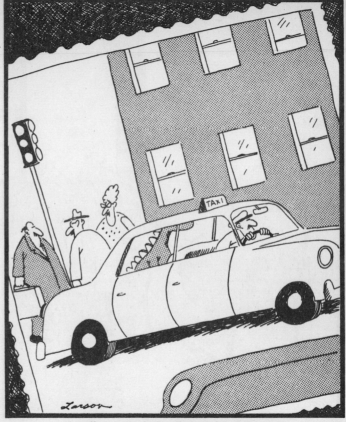

Another unsubstantiated photograph of the Loch Ness monster (taken by Reuben Hicks, 5/24/84, Chicago)

Impolite as they were, the other bears could never help staring at Larry's enormous deer gut.

"Oh, boy! The 'Nerd'! ... Now my collection's complete!"

68

"It's the same dream night after night ...
I walk out on my web, and suddenly a foot
sticks — and then another foot sticks, and
another, and another, and another ..."

"A few cattle are going to stray off in the morning,
and tomorrow night a stampede is planned around
midnight. Look, I gotta get back. ... Remember,
when we reach Santa Fe, I ain't slaughtered."

**Dial-a-Cat**

"Well, the sloth nailed him ... y'know,
ol' Hank never was exactly a 'quick draw.'"

"Blow, Howie, blow! ... Yeah, yeah, yeah!
You're cookin' now, Howie! ... All right! ...
Charlie Parker, move over! ... Yeah!"

Through a gross navigational error, the *Love Boat* steams into the Strait of Hormuz.

"Hey, Norton! ... Ain't that your dog attackin' the president?"

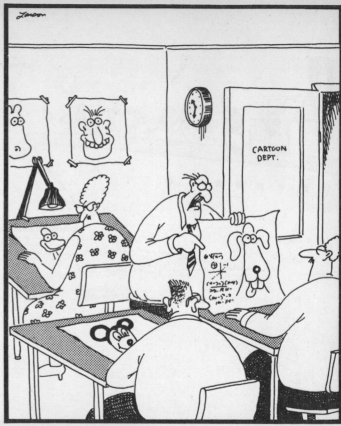

"Hey! What's this, Higgins? Physics equations? ... Do you enjoy your job here as a cartoonist, Higgins?"

"For crying out loud, Warren ... Can't you just
beat your chest like everyone else?"

Where all the young farm animals go to smoke

"Do I like it? Do I *like* it? ... Dang it, Thelma,
you know my feelings on barbed wire."

Crow kids

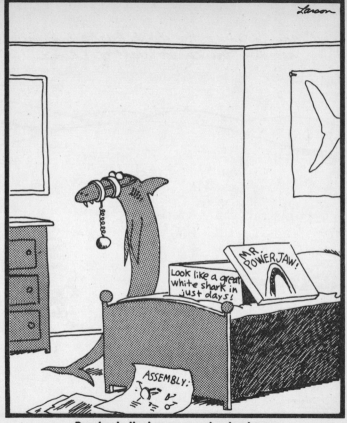

**Products that prey on shark wimps**

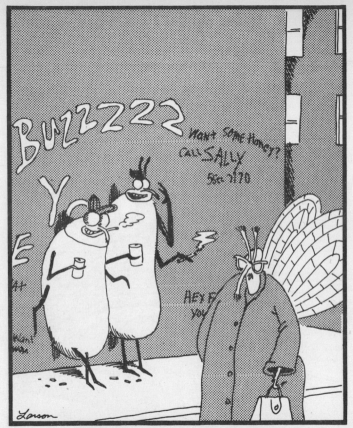

Killer bees are generally described
as starting out as larvae delinquents.

"Indians!"

**Ornithology 101 field trips**

**Mutants on the *Bounty***

Wildlife preserves

"More worms? ... Saaaaaaaaay — why are you being so nice to me all of a sudden?"

How cow documentaries are made

"Vince! Just trample him! ... He's drawing you into his kind of fight!"

"Yes! Yes! That's it! ... Just a little higher."

Mr. Ed spills his guts.

"Well, this is getting nowhere fast."

When piranha dine out

"Well, if I'm lucky, I should be able to get off this thing in about six more weeks."

"Again? You just had a
glass of water 12 days ago."

In the Old West, vegetarians were
often shot with little provocation.

87

"Won't talk, huh? ... Frankie! Hand me that scaler."

"This is it, Jenkins. ... Indisputable proof that the Ice Age caught these people completely off guard."

When jellyfish travel at unsafe speeds

"Shoot! Drain's clogged. ... Man, I hate
to think what might be down there."

"Now this is ... this is ... well,
I guess it's another snake."

"Oh my God! ... Murray's attacking
the bathroom mirror!"

"And so you just threw everything together?
... Mathews, a posse is something
you have to *organize*."

Animal horoscopes

Anthro horror films

Humpty Dumpty's final days

Java man       Peking man

Cro-Magnon man       Jazz man

**Hominid reconstructions**

"You know, it was supposed to be just a story about a little kid and a wolf . . . but off and on, I've been dressing up as a grandmother ever since."

"Now open even wider, Mr. Stevens. . . . Just out of
curiosity, we're going to see if we can also cram
in this tennis ball."

Suddenly, through forces not yet fully understood,
Darren Belsky's apartment became the center of a
new black hole.

"And when the big moment comes, here's the nursery Robert and I have fixed up."

Kangaroo nerds

The conversation had been brisk and pleasant when, suddenly and simultaneously, everyone just got dog tired.

"You're sick, Jessy! ... Sick, sick, sick!"

"For God's sake, hurry, driver! ... She's dropping babies all over the place!"

Cat showers

"Oh my gosh, Linda! ... I think your
Barbie's contemplating suicide!"

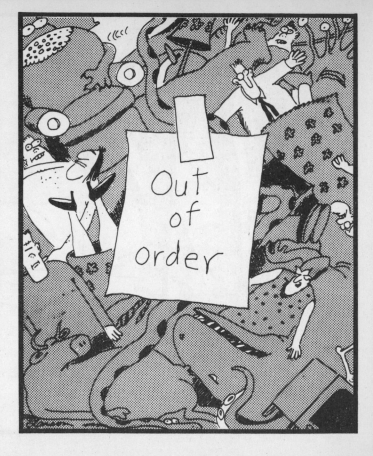

| | | |
|---|---|---|
| ☐ Beyond The Far Side | Gary Larson | £4.99 |
| ☐ Bride of The Far Side | Gary Larson | £4.99 |
| ☐ The Chickens Are Restless | Gary Larson | £5.99 |
| ☐ Cows of Our Planet | Gary Larson | £5.99 |
| ☐ The Curse of Madame "C" | Gary Larson | £5.99 |
| ☐ The Far Side | Gary Larson | £4.99 |
| ☐ The Far Side Gallery | Gary Larson | £7.99 |
| ☐ The Far Side Gallery 2 | Gary Larson | £7.99 |
| ☐ The Far Side Gallery 3 | Gary Larson | £7.99 |
| ☐ The Far Side Gallery 4 | Gary Larson | £7.99 |
| ☐ The Far Side Observer | Gary Larson | £4.99 |
| ☐ Hound of The Far Side | Gary Larson | £4.99 |
| ☐ In Search of The Far Side | Gary Larson | £4.99 |
| ☐ It Came from The Far Side | Gary Larson | £4.99 |
| ☐ The PreHistory of The Far Side | Gary Larson | £9.99 |
| ☐ Unnatural Selections | Gary Larson | £5.99 |
| ☐ Valley of The Far Side | Gary Larson | £4.99 |
| ☐ Wiener Dog Art | Gary Larson | £5.99 |
| ☐ Wildlife Preserves | Gary Larson | £4.99 |

Warner Books offers all the *Far Side* books by Gary Larson which can be ordered from the following address:
    Little, Brown and Company (UK) Limited
    P.O. Box 11,
    Falmouth,
    Cornwall TR10 9EN.
Alternatively you may fax your order to the above address.
Fax No. 0326 376423.

Payments can be made as follows: cheque, postal order (payable to Little, Brown and Company) or by credit cards, Visa/Access. Do not send cash or currency. UK customers and B.F.P.O. please allow £1.00 for postage and packing for the first book, plus 50p for the second book, plus 30p for each additional book up to a maximum charge of £3.00 (7 books plus).

Overseas customers including Ireland, please allow £2.00 for the first book, plus £1.00 for the second book, plus 50p for each additional book.

NAME (Block Letters) ...............................................................

.........................................................................................

ADDRESS ...........................................................................

.........................................................................................

.........................................................................................

☐ I enclose my remittance for _____

☐ I wish to pay by Access/Visa Card

Number ☐☐☐☐☐☐☐☐☐☐☐☐☐☐☐☐

Card Expiry Date ☐☐☐☐